WHAT TO EAT WHEN YOU DON'T FEEL LIKE EATING

WHAT TO EAT WHEN YOU DON'T FEEL LIKE EATING

BY JAMES HALLER

Published by
ROBERT POPE FOUNDATION

Distributed by
LANCELOT PRESS LIMITED, Box 425,
HANTSPORT, NOVA SCOTIA

COVER ILLUSTRATION
An original work of art (actual size)
by Tom Forrestall

COVER DESIGN by Joan Sinclair

ISBN 0-88999-558-3
Published 1994
Second printing June 1994
Third printing August 1994
Fourth printing October 1994
Fifth printing January 1995
Sixth printing March 1995
Seventh printing May 1995
Eighth printing January 1996

DISTRIBUTED BY
Lancelot Press Limited
PO Box 425, Hantsport, NS B0P 1P0
Phone (902) 684-9129 Fax (902) 268-3685

This book is respectfully dedicated
to the memory of
Dr. Gus Dodge
who, with
Rosemary Coffin, Madelein Stucky,
Peggy Clark, Jean Jackson,
and Libby Feuer
lit the beacon at Seacoast Hospice
in Exeter, New Hampshire

Acknowledgements

I would like to express my gratitude to the following people for their inspiration in helping to make this book possible. Barbara Griffin, Frank Flanders, the volunteers at Seacoast Hospice, Dr. Gregg Furth, Elizabeth Kübler-Ross, Dottie Wilson and a special thanks to John Byrne for his hours of sympathetic and talented editing.

I also appreciate the careful reading given my manuscript, and for their supportive comments found at the beginning of this book, by Dr. Balfour M. Mount, Montreal, P.Q., and Dr. G. Ross Langley, Halifax, N.S. For valued assistance, a word of thanks to Gloria Repetto, R.N., who has had extensive experience working with cancer patients at the Victoria General Hospital in Halifax.

Contents

Foreword

by Dr. Balfour M. Mount,
CM, OQ, MD, FRCS(C)
Professor, Faculty of Medicine, McGill University;
Director Palliative Care Medicine,
Royal Victoria Hospital, Montreal, P.Q.

What a rich array of talents is brought to Hospice by our Volunteers! In James Haller, Seacoast Hospice in Exeter, New Hampshire, acquired a master chef ready to learn from those who are ill and their families; ready to respond with creative genius, simplicity, humour and considerable flare!

Too often, the pureed, tasteless culinary offerings that find their way to the bedside only add to the anorexic nightmare, depression and reinforced isolation of serious illness. "So much of my identity, my culture, my memories of community are tied to eating. Is there nothing that can be done for this loss of appetite; my lurking nausea; that metallic taste in my mouth?"

For those who know James Haller's other cookbooks, the pages that follow, with all their freshness and ingenuity, will come as no surprise. His wonderful blend of nutritional science, ecological wisdom and home spun common sense provides a host of practical ideas that have helped many in their search for quality time during dark days.

Haller writes, "It really is and always has been my intention to simplify the art of cooking, this wonderful and most subtle form of alchemy." No small goal. He aims to increase nutritional value/flavour/interest/enjoyment and at the same time decrease preparation time for the weary, over-taxed caregiver. Three cheers for James Haller! He has achieved his goal. But more than that, for in this delightful, unpretentious book Mr. Haller also teaches us something about the art of caring — for the very sick, the apparently well, and for the world we live in.

Preface

by Dr. G. Ross Langley,
MD, FRCP(C), FACP, FRCP (Edin.)
Professor of Medicine, Dalhousie University;
Senior Physician,
Victoria General Hospital, Halifax, N.S.

If that part of suffering occasioned by the loss of appetite can be aided in any way, we would surely all, spouses, parents, friends and physicians, be grateful. This is what James Haller promises in advising us what to prepare for loved ones who don't feel like eating.

Loss of appetite is one of the earliest symptoms of being ill, and to those who try to help the sick, one of the more distressing. On the other hand the return of appetite and of eating, even in small amounts, is encouraging.

There are many specific reasons why patient's don't feel like eating. But the end result is often the same, protein-calorie malnutrition, depletion of some micro nutrients and perhaps, more important, it contributes to the disquietude and suffering of patients and their loved ones.

To me as a physician, and one with a particular interest in oncology, Haller's approach is all about compassion and providing supportive care, one of the most important aspects of treatment. He takes time to be with the patients and he listens carefully to them. He learns how he might help, without being intrusive or overbearing; to be useful and loving within his area of expertise. And it is obvious from the anecdotes in the text that he has been helpful.

It is the hope of the Robert Pope Foundation that this account of one man's experience with sick people will be helpful to others.

Introduction

As a chef who has spent the greater portion of the past twelve years interacting, one on one, with people with life threatening illnesses, I knew instinctively, from the encounter with my first cancer patient that there was a need to feed sick people differently. The proper kind of food could either enhance the possibility of their recovery, or, if terminal, to make that time as pleasant as humanly possible to the very end.

From my experience I have found that certain foods are particularly well suited for those in life threatening situations. I have discovered, and in the following pages give specific examples, of food that brings comfort and enjoyment even to those in advanced stages of illness.

I also believe whatever the survival percentage may be, no matter how small, the individual should hang on to the fact that there are some who survive and that it is possible to be part of that group. I tell about vitamin A that helps to rebuild and about vitamin C that assists in healing. I want cancer patients, and their families, to know there are foods that promote recovery as well as being amazingly tasty. This book recommends easy-to-prepare recipes that are both enjoyable and life enhancing, that are exceptionally helpful to those whose illness has gone into remission and to all those who are on the road to recovery.

Now I want to share how I got started in this work and to tell, first of all, of my experience in giving food to some very sick people. Then we will look at various food combinations that are both delightful and nutritious.

This all began thirteen years ago, after I had spent a week-long workshop in Portland, Oregon, with Elizabeth Kübler Ross, internationally renowned for her work with critically ill patients. It was one of the most dramatic weeks of my life and I returned determined to work with hospice and the terminally ill. With this in mind I joined Seacoast Hospice in Exeter, New Hampshire.

During the hospice training program, I began driving a woman suffering from leukemia to her doctor's appointment once a week.

Sometimes we'd have a little extra time so I would take her to Annabelle's and buy her an ice cream. We'd drive over to the ocean and just sit, look at the sail boats and eat ice cream. It was simply two people quietly sharing a beautiful moment.

But the ice cream became very important for her. It was, first, a new ritual. That is an important thing to a person who is in the process of leaving forever all they have ever known and remembered and loved — a brand new ritual.

It was also a source of power.

"What flavour would you like today?" I'd ask.

"The doctor says I'm not supposed to have chocolate — what the hell does he know? If he was so smart he'd cure me! Get me a double mocha-chocolate chip!"

And sometimes it was a memory.

"Get me strawberry. God, we used to love strawberry ice cream," her smile brightened with the memory. "... take a gallon of it out on the boat, and a bottle of vodka. It was wonderful."

Sometimes I would experiment. I brought her sushi once — rice and raw fish wrapped up in dried seaweed. The nutritional content was (to me) intoxicating. The next day I phoned to see how she liked it.

"Well, I gave the raw fish to the cats, and after you get rid of the dried seaweed and put a little soy sauce on the rice it's not half bad."

The morning I came to be with her for the last time I asked what I could bring her.

"Apricot ice cream," she smiled, "a scoop of apricot ice cream."

I brought it back to her and fed her, a little spoonful at a time. We never spoke. She just stared at me and smiled and ate ice cream. We were two people quietly enjoying a lovely moment. And then, after a half dozen or so mouthfuls she whispered "enough" and fell asleep. And, a little while later, she vanished forever.

It is amazing to me that her last earthly desire was apricot ice cream. Ice cream, this staple of good times and celebration, made from milk and cream, is the universal symbol of maternal nurturing. The color "apricot" is a combination of orange and gold, the colors of change and fulfillment, and in Chinese culture the apricot is the symbol of death, refertilization and androgyny.

Shortly afterward I was brought together with a gentleman named Frank. The first question he asked after I had introduced myself was, "Are you here to talk about death?" That was, of course, the one question that had not been covered in the hospice training. Somewhat taken aback I answered, "Yes, and whatever else you want to talk about."

It was with Frank that I began to look at food for the cancer patient.

Once, quite by accident, I happened in just as they were bringing in his lunch — a large tray with generous and heaping portions of Salisbury steak with canned gravy, instant mashed potatoes, and beets that came from the same source as the gravy. And for dessert there was one of those pallid pieces of pears, again from a can. Frank pushed it all away. The enormous amount of food overwhelmed his fragile digestive tolerance. He felt nausea and disconnection and it depressed him. It also depressed his wife and his children because his inability to eat his meal was yet another reminder that Frank would soon be dead.

The mistakes of that meal were glaringly obvious to me.

My first reaction, partly because I was a cook, and partly because of my Polish upbringing which taught me that you never went anywhere without bringing a casserole, was to ask him if there was something I might fix for him, something special. Was there a favorite dish, or something he remembered from his childhood that he loved or something he'd like to try? The answer to all these inquiries was an unhappy negative. Then I suggested a "peach custard." I told him it was from an old Shaker recipe.

"A peach custard?" he asked. "Why, I never heard of that. Sounds good."

The next afternoon I brought him three little custard cups filled with a soft and creamy peach custard topped with a piped-on rosette of meringue flavored with a few drops of rose water. He loved it. He ate the whole thing, and later on the other two. And, for a few moments, in the last two weeks of his being, he and his family felt that life was still a connected thing.

What I had learned was that it was wrong to bring in a large tray with huge portions of food on it. It was wrong to intrude on someone during an eating time, particularly if that person is having physical difficulty in eating. Their embarrassment in being seen struggling to eat detracts from the nurturing effect of the food. I also learned that the introduction of something new, a food they have never heard of before, one that did not give the memory a chance to "turn off" the body to the food, was a right idea. And it ws also right to use fresh foods.

Looking at Nutrition

Naturally I wanted to make the correct foods filled with the perfect nutrients. Not knowing where to start, I picked up a copy of "Eating Hints. Recipes and tips for better nutrition during cancer treatment." This was a government publication from the Health and Human Services Department, and to a chef it was fascinating reading. The nutritional end of it might have seemed correct, but if their recipes and knowledge of cooking were any indication of their knowledge of health, then I feared for the other information as well.

"Cheesy Hamburger Casserole." A pound of ground beef with a can of Cheddar Cheese Soup and a cup of macaroni. That's what this government publication suggested.

I don't think you should do that for someone who is well let alone ill. I don't think you should open cans and feed them ground beef.

Speaking as a chef now, what I wanted for Frank was fresh and whole and pure and clean food simply because it was obvious that those were the ingredients that could aid getting the body into the best possible condition to receive the medications that, if they could not save, might at least ease the last days of his life.

I also knew this "fresh, whole and pure" cooking had to be simple, quick, inexpensive, and of the best possible quality with an uncomplicated understanding of the nutritional aspects of food. It all had to be there in such a way that anyone could understand it. And, most importantly, the food had to taste *incredible.* Not just good, but the food had to be *delicious.* It had to taste like it was doing something wonderful for you, because that's the essence of nurturing.

At the very end of Frank's life I brought him some homemade sherbet from my own raspberries sweetened with maple syrup off my own trees. He looked with amazement at the deep, almost purple magenta of the sherbet, and said: "Why, I've never eaten anything that color in my whole life."

Purple is the color of spirituality, and the raspberry signifies the culmination and result of one state and the seed of the next.

The next thing I did was to sign up for a class entitled "Patient Behavior: The Nutrition Connection" where I learned of the dangers of caffeine, (too much and you neutralize your vitamin intake and also run the risk of it affecting your medication), the healing powers of vitamins A, B, C, D, beta carotene, potassium, proteins and carbohydrates, calories and on and on. I also learned that one of the great problems with cancer is that it eats up calories and proteins at an alarming rate of speed and that most people who die of cancer really die of malnutrition. It was all basic information, but information I knew people who were caring for a cancer patient would never have the time to sit down and try to absorb. There had to be some easier way of getting the message to the cook.

The Color Connection

After two more workshops with Elizabeth Kübler-Ross and several other week-long self-analyzation programs, I attended a drawing workshop conducted by a Jungian analyst named Gregg Furth.

While there are many seductive theories connected with the drawings, and their interpretations, the most compelling, for me as a cook, was an understanding about what the colors signify. I immediately thought of fruits and vegetables. This color theory was introduced by Dr. Susan Bach who, many years ago, worked closely with Carl Jung.

For instance, orange, according to Dr. Bach, is the color of change. It's the color of autumn, when the year changes. It is also the color of sweet potatoes, pumpkin, squashes, cantaloupes, carrots, oranges, tangerines, apricots, nectarines, papayas, peaches — foods that all have one great common ingredient, Vitamin A, the vitamin that helps in the growth and repair of body tissue. That sounded like "change" to me.

Then I lumped all the green foods together, the yellow, reds, purples, etc. The greens had a preponderance of vitamins A and C and significant amounts of potassium. Vitamin A rebuilds, vitamin C helps in healing, and potassium is essential for all normal cell's work.

Green is the color of growth.

Purple is the color of spirituality. The one great thing that all purple fruits and vegetables have in common is potassium. Potassium is known as "soul" food because it is essential for the life of all the body's cells. Maybe that's why they call it soul food because it lets life seem a little less oppressive.

Sweet Potato Frappe

One of the first things I ever "concocted" using these principles was a "sweet potato frappe." In baking a sweet potato, when it's cool, put it into a blender with a little pure maple syrup or honey, a cup of soft tofu, and a cup of apricot nectar.

For those concerned solely with the nutritional aspects of food, that's a little more than four hundred calories, about seventeen grams of protein, thirty mg. of vitamin C, 551 mgs. of potassium and almost thirty thousand International Units (I.U.'s) of vitamin A. Most importantly, it is all natural, all pure, tastes great, and is not out of a can.

It was definitely the color of change.

Sometimes I added an egg that I had boiled for a minute to kill off any bacteria. This added even more proteins. If you add a raw egg you can bake it into a custard or you can freeze that custard into an ice cream. If you blend a little fresh mint into the frappe it becomes tastier for patients on chemotherapy and helps take that metallic taste away. Mint also helps digestion.

Green mint, the color of growth, is also a symbol of renewal.

Add cinnamon and it tastes like a liquid pumpkin pie, add vanilla and you arrive at still another taste. Leave out the eggs, add firm tofu, bake at a low heat and you have a non-lacteal, no egg custard.

It is not my intention here to minimize or overly simplify the mysteries of good nutrition. But as important as it is for people to understand healthy cooking, it can also become one more burden for people contending with anger, confusion, panic, guilt, hopelessness, and grief — all the emotions by which people with cancer and other life threatening diseases, and their caregivers, are preoccupied. And, in cases of people dying with AIDS, there is also the added and overwhelming sense of being very expendable to an unsympathetic, uncaring government and a mean and accusing moral orthodoxy.

I would like to see anyone pick up a scientific tome and begin trying to memorize the nutrient values of foods when they are experiencing very trying emotions. But, it's very easy when a patient asks, "What should I eat?" to say, "Lots of orange colored foods, lots of dark greens — as many calories as you can and as many non-meat proteins." Almost everyone understands that.

With this concept in mind and armed solely with an electric frying pan and a blender, I began to teach cooking classes to hospice groups, cancer patients and families of cancer patients. The emphasis was on "simple" — how simple it is to cook, how simple it is to make delicious foods, how very simple it is to make nutritional foods. And how important it is to be able to do this cooking quickly.

The reason for this is that often a husband or a wife or someone seriously ill would suggest the patient's favorite dish, go out to the kitchen after shopping for all the right foods, spend an hour cooking it, and filling the house with wonderful and reminiscent aromas. By the time it's brought into the sick room, the nauseated patient has absolutely no tolerance for the dish and must push it away. Imagine the guilt the patient suffers and the disappointment the caregiver goes through!

But you could walk into the kitchen and in less than ten minutes create a wonderful fish soup made from a bottle of clam broth, a little white fish, some chopped broccoli and carrots, and beautiful red and yellow bell pepper. This the patient could eat, enjoy, and begin to get all the benefits from something wonderful long before some negative anticipation even gets an opportunity to start.

From a chef's perspective, my concern is the overuse of additives and preservatives, too much sugar, too much salt. Caffeine, deep fried foods, instant foods and junk food are sometimes used as comfort foods, but should be avoided if possible.

Almost everything in the fresh produce department seems to be the right choice. If the produce has been sent from some far off land (just check the box it comes in), then get the frozen product instead. Food that is picked too early and left to ripe in a box in transit simply does not taste good, and, if it has no taste, how nutritious can it be? Very often frozen food can be not only tastier but more nutritious. Nothing, however, can surpass the food locally grown and recently picked, and nothing is more beneficial.

The point of all this is not only to provide the most perfect foods possible, either to promote recovery or to make these last times as wonderful as possible, but to give more control to the patient and to the family. The caregivers can know that at least, in this area they are doing everything humanly possible for their patient.

They can easily learn how to make sweet potato frappe, instant fish stew, instant salmon mousse cooked in an electric fry pan, to use tofu and how to make it non-Oriental, fruit patitas (Cuban fruit drinks with ice and milk), and how to serve small amounts of food several times a day. Knowing the significance and "meaning" of the ingredients in food may be helpful for some people.

Foods that have the highest nutrient content should be used — turnip greens, spinach, bok choy, broccoli, beet greens, collards. These should be chopped small and sautéed either in olive oil with garlic and lemon, or gently simmered in a little chicken broth, or added to fish stews. These are all vegetables that cook in less than five minutes, retain a wonderful healthy green color, and are filled with nutrition. And all the cook has to remember is "dark green."

The same simple approach applies to all the orange colored vegetables and fruits, whether steaming, baking or stewing. These include sweet potatoes, carrots and apricot soufflés.

Of course, if you say "soufflé" the average person slinks out of the kitchen in embarrassed fear, thanks to the European school of cooking that insists that a cook also be a chemist.

Soufflé! Simply egg whites with something in it. Puree a cup of cooked carrots with an egg yolk, or maybe a half cup of firm tofu, add some cinnamon, a little honey and maybe some salt and pepper. Whip up four or five egg whites until you've got a soft meringue, fold in the pureed carrots, and plop it into a buttered baking dish. Put it in the oven at about 400F/204C degrees and let it cook twenty minutes to a half hour. Soufflé!

For those who cannot eat whole foods and must rely on pureed edibles there are also ways to make these more palatable.

Pureed spaghetti pushed through a pastry bag can look like spaghetti again. Pureed meatballs scooped with a melon baller become meat balls again. Other vegetables put through a pastry gun (for example, peas for leaves, and carrot flowers) create food that is colorful and, simply arranged, can look more tasteful and appealing than a glass of something someone gives you with a straw and tells you, "This is beef stew."

It really is and always has been my intention to simplify the art of cooking, this wonderful and most subtle form of alchemy.

Food is even wonderful when you're not eating it. I once was with a hospice patient who simply could not eat much food at all. In fact everything she took was a liquid, but she loved to hear about food.

"Tell me what you cooked this evening."

And so I'd go through the night's menu. "For a soup I did a chilled blueberry and lavender buttermilk cream soup, and for the appetizer there was a choice between an egg roll stuffed with a salmon and white fish mousse in a cilantro tomato sauce or escargot in a sambucca mayonnaise. The relief course was a minted pea sherbet. We had roast duck in raspberries and cream d'cassis, ratatouille and roasted herbed potatoes and carrots. And for dessert, strawberries, sour cream and brown sugar.

She would smile, and "tsk," and shake her head and say, "Oh my," and "Ohhh, that sounds just delicious." She was astonished at the combinations and creations and laughed out loud. And yet she never once was able to eat even a single bite of it.

We never know, as hospice volunteers, just exactly what it is that we do. We're never quite certain if we are there for the patient or for the family. As I look back on my experiences it's hard to know if all those people loved me because I listened or because I held their hand and gave them encouragement, and even sometimes prayed with them, or if they loved me because I brought them a scoop of ice cream, or simply told them a recipe. I only know, because I could feel it, that they loved me.

Hours before Frank died, he took my hand and placed it on his heart and told me, "I will never, ever forget you. You sure are some cook!"

I believe the cure for all ailments, other than broken bones, can be found in the garden, in the forests and, of course, in the kitchen. What we need to look at and speak about, in order for this to one day become a reality, are the pollutants caused by industry, an apathetic government that supports that industry, and an even more apathetic community of consumers that allows these agencies to continue to produce destruction. We must end the destruction of our water supplies, the air we breathe, the ground in which we grow our food, and ultimately, the destruction of humanity.

A Word About the Recipes and Use of This Book

What I have tried to do is create a short, concise guide to the best foods you can eat during a catastrophic illness and to show you an easy, convenient way to cook those foods. There are hundreds of long, intelligently written books on nutrition, organic cooking, and cooking during an illness. Having worked for twelve years on a one-to-one basis with cancer patients it is my experience that many people going through an illness, whether as patient or caregiver, are so consumed by the illness that they have neither time nor inclination to pick up a four hundred page volume filled with nutritional jargon that to the neophyte is (sometimes) incomprehensible. If, however, through this short book you are motivated to go forward and explore the more intricate areas of fine nutritional cooking then I applaud you.

Dark Green Foods

The Leafy Greens —

Beet Greens, Chinese Cabbage, Swiss Chard, Collards, Kale, Spinach, Turnip Greens

All the dark green foods have in common a preponderance of vitamin A and Potassium. Vitamin A promotes healing, potassium makes you feel better. Greens are easy and quick to prepare, usually within minutes. The leafy greens, in general, taste best and deliver the most nutrition if they are cooked in their own juices rather than steamed or boiled.

Chop 1 pound of greens
heat a skillet with two tablespoons of olive oil,
add one tablespoon fresh, finely chopped garlic,
add the greens, turn heat low and cover for
about ten minutes.
Uncover and stir, cooking until all the greens
are limp.

If you cannot tolerate the olive oil use a half cup

of chicken or beef stock, or, use nothing at all. Simply add the chopped greens to a skillet, turn the heat on medium low and cover. They will cook in their own juices. Salt and pepper, garlic, lemon juice — these are all added according to one's taste and digestive toleration. Note: Chards, collards, kales and turnip greens, being a little tougher, might take a minute or two longer to tenderize in the cooking.

All Leafy Greens and Chicken Soup

Let me first begin by saying it is a good thing to have some stock in the house. Secondly, let me say that it is one of the easiest, most inexpensive things to make and the rewards far outnumber the effort, especially if you're cooking for someone who is going through a serious illness. Making chicken stock is simply making chicken soup, straining out the meat and vegetables and then putting the liquid away in the freezer in small quantities ready for use whenever you need it.

Green Onion Chicken Stock

2 cups chopped green onions (scallions)
1 3 to 5 pound chicken
2 cups chopped carrots
2 cups fresh chopped parsley
water, three times as much as will cover chicken

Put all the ingredients into a pot, place the heat on the low side of medium, cover and let simmer for about three to four hours. Strain off the liquid, and put it away in one and two pint-sized glass containers, leaving about an inch and a half room at the top for expansion when it freezes. I try to avoid plastic in every instance because I can always taste the plastic and, if I can taste the plastic, I wonder what else besides the taste I'm getting.

Any of the Leafy Greens Soup

2 cups chopped greens
2 cups stock
salt and pepper to taste
2 tablespoons chopped fresh parsley

Chop the greens into small, easily edible pieces, place them into the stock, season with salt and pepper, heat until boiling, turn down to a simmer and let cook about four minutes. If salt is not part of the diet, use a little lemon juice and a sprinkle of oregano, basil or tarragon.

To enhance the nutrient value of this soup, add a cup of chopped carrots or sweet potatoes to the stock, and let them simmer until soft, then add one cup of the greens instead of two, and let the soup simmer until the greens are soft and palatable.

Bell peppers, red or yellow, chopped small and added to the soup not only make the soup that much healthier but add beautiful color.

There once was a time when we were told that the more color on our plate the healthier the meal. This is still true. Imagine what a terrific thing it would be if while you were eating this food you could concentrate, almost meditate on what was happening while eating: "... the green leaves symbolize renewal, their color is growth; the sweet potatoes and carrots are the color of change, the yellow bell peppers are energy. This food is helping to heal. It is rebuilding and regenerating my body."

When you consider that food is our fuel, the substance that makes the body run, that causes the brain to work, this concept is not so far fetched.

Broccoli

This is a wonderful vegetable that, the medical profession is finally admitting, has the possibility of preventing cancer. This, of course, sounds too easy and almost a panacea. It is a great vegetable and one anyone going through an illness should be eating.

During the Bush administration, Mr. Bush was quoted as "hating broccoli." This was a strange comment to make since broccoli is the color of growth and the symbol of regeneration, two important factors to think about when you are eating this wonderful vegetable (or your country is going through a recession). Don't eat just the floweret of this plant. Learn to peel the stalks and use them as well. The entire vegetable is filled with vitamin A and potassium.

First cut off the very ends of the stalks about an inch up from the bottom. They are usually too tough to be tasty. Then, using a potato peeler, peel the stalks of the broccoli starting from the bottom of the stalk and working up toward the flowered end. It's just like peeling carrots. The "skin" on the tiny branches that hold the flowers is usually thin enough to be tender when cooked. Again, you might want to steam the vegetable, or you might want to simply gently sauté it in a couple of tablespoons of olive oil with a little salt and pepper, and some lemon or lime juice, and a couple of chopped cloves of garlic. Or again, chopping the broccoli and the stalks into smaller, easier to eat pieces, you might sauté them in a pint of chicken stock.

Non-Fat Cream Soups Using Leafy Greens

By using powdered milk, thickened with a little flour, the addition of white wine (if tolerable), nutmeg, and salt and pepper, you can achieve a creamy, great tasting base for any of the leafy vegetables, either as a "creamed vegetable dish" or a cream soup. I try to avoid "soup bases" simply because boullion generally contains MSG and other additives. Once again, if you have a pint of homemade chicken stock in the freezer it would be a great thing to add to the soup. Instead of using water to mix with the powdered milk, use the chicken stock instead. The result is not totally fat free (two cups of chicken broth amount to somewhat less than 3 grams of fat) but you've added some protein to the dish and the taste is great.

Any Leafy Green Cream Soup (low fat)

2 cups chicken stock (or water for a no-fat soup)
1 cup powdered milk
1/4 cup flour
1/4 cup chopped fresh parsley
1/2 teaspoon ground nutmeg

Put all the ingredients into a blender and blend until smooth. Pour it into a small pot and bring to a simmer, stirring often. Because there is no fat in this cream soup you have to keep stirring it so that it doesn't stick and scorch on the bottom of the pot. Add two cups of any chopped leafy green and cook until the greens are soft enough to eat. Add salt and pepper to taste.

If the diet and medications permit, add 1/4 cup of dry white wine to the soup when you first put it into the pot. This will give it time to cook off the alcohol and you leave a wonderful taste. I can't repeat this enough: the food must taste terrific, as though it's doing something equally terrific for the patient! One of the devastating things about a hospital stay or a long illness is the food you're forced to eat — it continually reminds you that you're sick.

Sweet Peppers

There does not seem to be a lot of data on the incredible nutrient value of sweet peppers, yet, even though they are not always easy to digest they do contain a fair amount of vitamin C. So, as an advocate of that vitamin and its healing properties, I suggest you try to get as much of it as possible from natural sources. Chopping bell peppers into soups, stews and vegetable dishes can only enhance any healing that might be taking place due to right eating.

Orange Foods

Vegetables —

Carrots, Sweet Potatoes and Yams

Carrots, Sweet Potatoes and Yams are the orange vegetables that have the highest content of vitamin A. One cup of cooked carrots contains over 30,000 I.U.'s of vitamin A., a cup of carrot juice almost 25,000 I.U.'s. The important thing to know is that you are getting this vitamin from these vegetables. Yellow and red bell peppers are also a source of beta-carotene, a provitamin with potent effects which may prevent the development of some cancers.

The above vegetables can be eaten by themselves, mixed with greens or rice or even beans, or blended into sauces or juice drinks. It might, at first, seem boring to use the same four or five vegetables, day in and day out, and try to vary them, but once you begin to experiment, you'll find an almost endless array of satisfying, healthy and, most of all, tasty dishes.

Carrots

If you are growing the carrots yourself, or know that they come from an organic garden, then keep the peelings in when you cook them. The peelings are a great source of minerals. Many people who grow their own carrots treat them like parsnips and let them stay underground well into the winter until the first thaw. I find carrots sweeter than those picked before the first frost.

When I cook carrots I slice them thinly (so they cook fast). I don't cover them with water because I don't want to cook all the nutrients out and throw them down the drain. I like a little water on the bottom of the cooking pan and I like the pan covered and the heat on medium. You have to stir them around from time to time to prevent sticking, and you might want to add a tablespoon of olive oil. Toward the end of the cooking, usually about eight to ten minutes, I'll add a couple of tablespoons of honey or pure maple syrup, or even frozen orange concentrate. If I'm cooking for someone going through chemo I'll also add a tablespoon or two of fresh mint. The mint will help in alleviating the metallic taste that so often accompanies chemotherapy.

The use of frozen concentrates can be invaluable! They not only add a healthier sweetener, but they impart new and interesting tastes to the same old foods, add attractiveness from their color, and some nutrient value. They are also convenient and inexpensive. (If people could find all this in another person, marriage rates would triple!) Try carrots in a cranberry or cherry concentrate, sweet potatoes in orange concentrate, turnips in apple concentrate, any of the above in a white grape juice concentrate — mix them around, experiment with different things, surprise patients with something they've never heard of or eaten before. It might be just the thing to bring an appetite back.

Sweet Potatoes

This versatile vegetable is a pure, safe and delicious source of copious amounts of vitamin A. Baked and peeled, it is tasty just as it is, or a little pure honey or maple syrup can be dribbled on it. It can be mashed with an egg to add protein, cut and diced into soups and stews, mixed with greens and peppers, made into pies and custards and blended into tofu with apricot nectar to create a great no lacteal, no egg custard that still has protein.

Steamed Sweet Potatoes

If you don't have a steamer simply use a colander or large strainer over a pot of simmering water and cover. Peel and thinly slice one or two medium sized sweet potatoes or yams. Put them into the steamer and let them cook long enough, maybe fifteen minutes, until they soften to the touch of a fork.

While they are still hot you might want to mash them with a fork and sprinkle a little honey or pure maple syrup, about a tablespoon or so, across the potatoes. Sometimes people with an illness have a very low threshold to sweeteners. If this is the case then the potato will be sweet enough by itself.

It is always a good rule to ask the patient how it tastes. Is it too sweet? How does it sit in your stomach? What does it need for you to enjoy it? Don't be put off by negative replies or rejections as that is the only way you're going to be able to know how to feed the person better.

Baked Sweet Potatoes

I like to bake them before peeling, then peel them when fresh out of the oven. Since baking is such a dry heat I feel this process retains the most nutrients. After baking one or two medium sized sweet potatoes, peel them, put them into a baking dish and add about

1/2 cup chopped fresh apricots
1/2 cup apricot juice
1 or 2 tablespoons of honey or pure maple syrup

Return to the oven covered and bake another fifteen minutes at about 400 F. or 204 C. Uncover and serve.

Winter Squashes —

Acorn, Hubbard, Turks Head, Banana, Butternut, Golden Delicious, and Pumpkin

Baked, steamed or simmered in a little stock, any of these winter squashes, filled with vitamin A, can be easily prepared.

Acorn Squash

Cut them in half, clean out the seeds, turn them upside down in a baking pan, cover and bake at 400 F/204 C for about a half hour to forty-five minutes (depending on their size). Take them out of the oven, scoop out the meat, add seasoning and serve. The seasoning, again, might be a little salt and pepper, a little orange concentrate, perhaps some honey or pure maple syrup, a combination of all the above, or any inventiveness on your part.

I suggest this method because peeling, dicing and steaming or lightly boiling, while all good methods of cooking, are just a little more time consuming. Once again, part of the purpose of this book is to help make the care of the patient as easy and non-time consuming as possible since there are so many things to do that take up your time. All the winter squash can easily be prepared by this same method of halving, cleaning out the seeds, turning them upside down and baking.

Winter Squash Soups

Some of the squashes (I'm thinking of butternut now) have so much of their own liquid that often all you have to do to make a nice soup is puree the meat in a blender, add a little seasoning, and you have a great soup. But for those of you who need a little more specific information I suggest:

1 cup of stock
1/4 cup chopped green onions
1/4 cup fresh chopped parsley
dash of nutmeg
salt and pepper to taste

Puree all the ingredients, return to a pan and bring to a simmer, cooking for about eight to ten minutes. This is a no lacteal, no fat soup.

To make this a no fat cream soup, simply add:

1 cup powdered milk to the soup before pureeing.

Stuffed Squash

The Acorn Squash is ideal for stuffing and baking. Cut them in half and scoop out the seeds, bake them upside down for about a half hour at 400 F/204 C covered. Remove from the oven, turn them rightside up and fill with a combination of chopped greens, peppers, carrots and a little stock. Since the cavities hold so little add a mix of

1 finely chopped carrot
1 finely chopped red bell pepper
1 cup finely chopped greens (broccoli or cauliflower)
1 cup of stock
1/2 cup powdered milk (optional)
salt and pepper to taste

This will easily fill the two or even four halves. Cover the squash, return to a 400 F/204 C oven and bake another twenty minutes to a half hour.

Some people will ask, "Why not make a lot of food and keep it in the refrigerator or freezer until ready to eat?" While it is true that that might make the preparation easier, I am thinking of the freshness, not just because of the nutrients, but also because of the taste. People going through an illness often have a high sensitivity to taste. Food that sits in the refrigerator for a day begins to taste old, or pick up the tastes from other foods, making it unappealing.

Sweet Potato Frappe (shake)

In a blender put

1 medium sized baked sweet potato
1 1/2 cups apricot nectar
1/2 cup soft tofu
pure honey or pure maple syrup to taste

Blend until smooth and creamy (for patients on chemotherapy the addition of fresh mint might help to take away the metallic taste from the drug). You could also add 2 eggs well beaten and then bake at 300 F/ 149 C in a pan of water for about forty-five minutes. This will turn it into a custard. You can also freeze this custard into an ice cream.

For a no lacteal, no egg custard:

1 medium sized baked sweet potato
1 cup soft tofu
1 cup pure apricot nectar

2 to 3 tablespoons of honey or pure maple syrup
1 teaspoon vanilla

Blend all the ingredients until smooth, place in a baking dish and bake at 325 F/165 C (uncovered) for about forty-five minutes to an hour.

Serve either warm or chilled or freeze it into an ice cream.

Pumpkin Pie Frappe

1 medium baked sweet potato or 1 cup cooked fresh pumpkin
1/2 teaspoon cinnamon
1 teaspoon lemon juice
1 cup apricot nectar

Blend until smooth.

Vanilla Frappe

Use above ingredients but substitute

1 teaspoon pure vanilla for the other flavorings
and
1 cup pure pear nectar instead of apricot.

Experiment as much as you like.

The Orange Fruits

Apricot, Mango, Cantaloupe, Casaba, Muskmelon, Nectarines, Oranges, Papaya, Peach

Some of these fruits, fresh and ripe and in season, should be in the house at all times for snacking. They are filled with vitamin A and C and potassium. Dried apricots and dried peaches are always available and, while they don't have the highest content of vitamin A, they are good for you. Mangos and papayas are great for digestion and, of course, all the citrus fruits help in elimination which is very necessary during illnesses, particularly if the patient is involved in some pain relieving medication which seems to always create constipation. One of the best foods to help with that problem is the use of pure olive oil. Even when making fruit drinks, you might want to add a tablespoon of olive oil to the drink. The taste disappears in the mix.

Apricot, Nectarine, Peach or Apple Custard

The following is based on an old Shaker recipe. I've changed it around, cut back on the sugar and taken the butter out altogether, but the custard that remains is simply wonderful. You can make this as a pie, or put it into a Pyrex baking dish, or a soufflé dish, or any oven-proof dish you have in the house that will hold it. I generally parcel the recipe out into small ramekins and serve them one at a time. They easily stay fresh and healthy for a couple of days if well covered, but usually they can be eaten in a day because of their size and good taste.

2 cups of any of the above fruits, raw and chopped small
1 cup sugar
juice of 1 lemon
4 whole eggs
2 egg yolks
reserve the white of two eggs

Put the fruit into the baking dish (or evenly portioned into ramekins). Beat the other ingredients (save the egg whites), pour onto the fruit and bake at 325 F/165 C for about 30 minutes. If using ramekins only bake about fifteen to twenty minutes — test the custard with a touch of your finger. If they seem firm remove them. Whip the whites into a meringue with

2 tablespoons of sugar
2 tablespoons rosewater

Dollop the meringue on the custard and return to the oven at 400 F/204 C for another few minutes until the meringue begins to brown a tiny bit.

For a completely smooth custard, puree the fruit with the other ingredients until smooth, then pour into the baking dish and follow the same instructions.

Fruit Drinks

Any Fresh Fruit Patita

2 cups any fresh fruit (berries, plums, apricots, bananas, melons, mango, papaya, etc.
1 cup skim milk
1 cup powdered milk
Tablespoon honey
a few ice cubes

Combine all the ingredients in a blender and blend at a high speed until smooth. Again, you might want to add a little mint for some patients on chemotherapy.

For a complete no lacteal drink omit the milk and the powdered milk and add a little juice or cider instead.

Juices In General

If you have a juice machine use it as much as you can. Carrots are wholesome, any of the dark orange colored fruits and vegetables and any of the dark greens made into juices are good for you. The problem is making some of these juices taste good!

Green juices, or juice from what we generally know as "green vegetables" don't often translate into a tasty "sweet" drink. A little stock, either hot or cold, brings a more "soup" like taste to the juice. Other juices, that come from yellow and orange colored foods, are usually improved if they are given a sweet or salty taste. Sometimes you might want to add different juices. Apple mixed with carrot or, better yet, apricot nectar mixed with carrot juice, a little mint and some honey can offer the patient a taste that is not only new but one that will deliver a powerhouse of vitamin A and carotene, both nutrients essential in fighting disease.

Proteins

I am omitting meats as a source of proteins simply because I prefer to use vegetable proteins found in brown rice, beans and tofu. It is also commonly known that, in order to get the most from these proteins, certain foods must be eaten in conjunction with other foods. The combinations are relatively easy to remember: rice and beans, cereals with milk, legumes soup with bread. There are, of course, more complicated combinations (that also offer a lot more variety) but these are the easiest to remember.

Cooking Beans

The reason we are taught to soak beans overnight is because it tenderizes the bean and makes the fiber and rich nutrients more available. If you simply boil the beans, they are tougher and you run the risk of losing a lot of their goodness.

Black beans, pinto beans, white beans, lentils, the longer they are cooked, the softer they are to eat, the less gas they are likely to produce. Chewing on caraway seeds is said to help gas problems.

Cooking the Beans

Rinse, then cover the beans with cold water and let sit overnight. When ready to cook, add enough water to the beans to cover them, bring to a boil and gently boil until the beans are tender.

2 cups beans
water to cover
1 cup chopped green onions
1/2 cup fresh chopped parsley
salt and pepper to taste

Gently boil for about 1 hour or until beans are tender. Here they can be mixed with rice, or served as a side dish to rice, or mixed with rice and greens in a soup.

White Enriched Rice

Cooked plain or lightly flavored, rice, without butter or oil, is an alternate source of proteins, carbohydrates and calories and is simple to make and adds a little variety to soups. Brown rice is higher in proteins.

1 cup brown rice
1 tablespoon olive oil
3 cups of water
1 lemon cut in half

Place all the ingredients into a pot large enough to hold five cups, bring to a boil, cover and turn down to a simmer. Let cook for about fifty minutes to an hour. Turn off the heat and let sit for about ten minutes. Uncover and fluff with a fork. This will make about four cups of cooked brown rice. Add any seasoning you prefer, mix with chopped cooked greens and orange vegetables, or add it to soups. This makes a great side dish alone or mixed with vegetables.

Grains and Cereals

Whole Wheat Total is one of the best prepared cereals for nutritional value. If you cannot tolerate milks, try eating the cereal with orange juice or apple juice or apricot nectar or almond milk or even a soy product. Best of all you might want to try making your own "granola." Of course, as soon as you mention that "G" word, half the world wants to run in the other direction. On the other hand you can create a really incredible cereal filled with all kinds of healing foods, that taste great, is not expensive, and is really very simple to make. My only problem with this is that you sometimes have to make several pounds at a time which means keeping it in the freezer or giving a lot away.

1/2 pound wheat bran
1/4 pound wheat germ

1/2 pound soy flakes
1/2 pound wheat flakes
1/2 pound oat flakes
1/2 pound rye flakes
1/2 pound natural flaked coconut
1/2 pound chopped almonds

Spread all of the above into a large cookie sheet, dribble a cup of pure maple syrup or honey across it, and bake in a pre-heated 400 F/ 204 C oven for about ten to fifteen minutes, mixing it around from time to time so that the toasting is even. If it takes a little more than fifteen minutes, keep your eye on it. The toasted taste is definitely worth the effort.

When the toasting is done add a half pound each of

chopped raisins
dates
prunes
dried papaya
dried apricots

Mix well and store in the freezer.

One of the interesting things you might want to try, if you have a food processor, is to put a cup of this mix into the processor and, with the chopping blade, process it almost until it becomes a flour. Then peel grapefruit or oranges, apples which don't have to be peeled, peaches or apricots, and slice them about a half inch thick, dip them in beaten egg, then dip them into the mix, and fry them in a little olive oil until they brown on both sides. Not only is this a new and great taste but the digestive properties connected to the granola and fruits are wonderful. I cannot stress how important elimination is during an illness. As Dr. Saunders, who started the Hospice movement, said, "Nothing matters more than the bowels!"

Tofu

One of the truly wonderful aspects of tofu is that it is the chameleon of the food world. By that I mean it will pick up the taste of whatever it is being cooked with. A little diced tofu added to cooked greens adds wonderful non-fat proteins, added to soups it tastes like a noodle, used in puddings it becomes a custard and put into drinks it turns into a milk shake.

Most people think of tofu as a mysterious food from the mysterious East, and in order to cook it you must be some mysterious person with a mysterious talent. However, in this particular instance, once you begin to consider it as a meat substitute, and treat it like it is meat, the mystery disappears.

Imitation Veal Amondine

For this recipe you'll need to buy what is known

as "firm" tofu. You can either buy it in a health food store or most supermarkets now carry a variety. Make certain you check the package to see that preservatives have not been added. It is usually packed in spring water. Remove the tofu and place it on a few layers of paper towel, then cover it with a few more layers of paper towel, and then put a heavy dish on top of that. This is a good way to drain out excess water and make the curd more solid for frying. You might want to let it sit like that for an hour or two.

When it comes time to use it, slice it about a third of an inch thick. Bread the slices in a beaten egg and some bran (prepared breadcrumbs generally are loaded with junk) and then fry them on a medium heat in

2 tablespoons olive oil
1/2 cup chopped green onions
1/4 cup chopped fresh parsley
1/4 cup sliced almonds

After you have browned the tofu on one side, turn it over and as you brown the other side you might also want to dribble across it the

juice of one lemon
salt and pepper to taste

This, in no way, is meant to fool anyone that it is veal. But it does "remind" you of the taste and what you are getting is a very healthy substitute for meat.

Fish Mousse Dumplings

Have a pan of water (stock of clam juice would be better) simmering on the stove. Into a blender add

2 egg whites
1 cup any fresh fish
salt and pepper to taste
fresh tarragon (or other fresh herb if you have it)
juice of half a lemon

Puree, then drop by spoonfuls into the simmering water. Cover, let cook about two minutes, turn the dumplings, cover again and let cook another couple of minutes. Remove from the stock and serve. Lots of proteins are in this dish.

You can use this same dumpling process simply by substituting anything you want for the fish and making vegetable, or even chicken, dumplings. You could do a cup of cooked mashed parsnips, cooked, finely chopped cauliflower and broccoli, cooked carrots, cooked potatoes, white and sweet, or a cup of cooked chopped chicken. If you need to thicken the mixture a little add some non-fat powdered milk. This will also add calories and proteins.

Chicken and Turkey

While the white meat of both these venerable birds is an excellent source of proteins and calories it is important to know that they have not been raised on chemicals, or been scratching around in PCB's, or dipped into some chemical to "keep their color nice." It is also important to remove any plastic timers that have been pounded into the bird, or other plastic devices to "hold" their little legs together. If you are cooking them, either roasting in the oven, or boiling in a soup, I think it is a good thing to remove their skin to make the finished product as fat free as possible. The cooked breast can either be eaten as it is, or chopped into soups. Stuffed into acorn squash along with the other suggested vegetables, sautéed with greens or mixed into rice and beans.

A small chicken, three to four pounds, or a

small turkey, eight to ten pounds, will provide enough white meat for a few meals for the patient and plenty of dark meat for anyone else. I prefer roasting for two reasons, the first being the taste, and the second because I think you will retain the most nutrients in the roasting because of a drier heat.

Roast Chicken

One 3 to 4 pound chicken

Remove the skin, salt and pepper to taste, sprinkle with crushed garlic, put it into a baking pan, cover it and place it in a 400 F/204 C oven and let cook for about an hour.

To make an entire meal add the following before you put it into the oven.

4 medium sized washed and cut in half sweet potatoes
1 medium sized onion cut in quarters
1 pound of trimmed green beans
1 head of washed and trimmed cauliflower or broccoli

Simply follow the above directions for cooking the chicken.

The same applies to cooking a turkey. Skin the bird, rub it down with some olive oil and herbs and salt and pepper, cook it, covered, in a 400 F/204 C oven for about 20 minutes per pound. Add your vegetables in the last hour of the cooking.

Personal Observations

This kind of cooking is healthy for the entire family and, if the entire family is eating with and at the same time as the patient, it is a sign that the patient has not become a separate unit from the family — that he/she is still a healthy part of the family. If, however, the patient is unable to eat with the family, here are some important things to remember.

1. The eating should be like a meditation. Understand what is going into your system, picture it working to your benefit. If you are eating the colors of "change" or "growth" admit this to yourself, remind yourself that you are bringing change into your system, that you are admitting the growth of new cells and tissues.

2. Don't listen to the news while you eat! The news is usually filled with disasters, hostility, sadness and death. Is that what you want going into your consciousness? Turn off the T.V. Better to listen to beautiful relaxing music. That old maxim, "Music hath charms to soothe the savage beast," has great truth. Music that you personally find beautiful truly does relax you, and when your body is relaxed it facilitates the system to work with more order. It helps the blood to move more freely through your veins, helps the medication, and the food, to provide what it is supposed to provide.

3. Drink plenty of distilled or pure spring water! If possible, avoid eating or drinking anything from plastic or cans. You might ask, "What research can you provide that leads you to that conclusion?" My answer is, "My taste!" If I can taste the plastic in a plastic container of water then what else am I getting? Cans? Are the cans aluminum? Are there additives and preservatives in the can goods? How long has the food been in that can?

4. Avoid additives and preservatives. Try to steer clear of foods that have been refined as

usually all the natural nutrients have been "refined" out of them.

5. Avoid chocolate, other solid fats, such as margarines, butter, lard, etc.

6. Caffeine, or too much of it, can neutralize your vitamin intake and might possibly hinder medications.

7. Don't walk into the patient's room with a tray loaded with food. Usually the patient's system/psyche will reject what looks like too much to assimilate. Bring small, healthy "snack" type portions several times a day. A little cup of wonderful soup and a tiny ramekin of custard, a small stuffed acorn squash filled with a beautiful mix of vegetables, half a bran muffin dribbled with honey, a small plate of a few well-cooked carrots, bright orange, and a stalk of bright green, gently cooked broccoli, a small piece of beautiful pink salmon that has been steamed or baked or poached — foods that look beautiful and are appealing so that the patient looks forward to the eating.

8. Find the things that make you laugh: your old favorite movies, T.V. re-runs, stories,

books, comedies. Be with people who make you feel good. Laughter is wonderful medicine!

9. Massage. Touch your friend. Rub their heads and their shoulders with a relaxing rub to ease tensions and anxieties. Bring tiny children in to visit the sick person. The pure and healthy energy of a child can perform wonders.

A Final Word

A doctor may say to a patient, "You have a life threatening illness and, of the people with this particular illness, this is the percentage that survives." Whatever that percentage, no matter how small it may seem, immediately assume that you are part of it. Your attitude toward yourself, the treatment, your diet, and your ability to recover are important factors.

More and more we learn that diet, meditation, visualization and attitude help people recover from what was once considered an automatic death sentence. If it works for some people, why can't it also work for you?

I wish you a kitchen filled with light!